DREAM
BELIEVE
ACHIEVE

JoJo Siwa

JoJo Siwa: Be You Journal
A CENTUM BOOK 978-1-911461-47-0
Published in Great Britain by Centum Books Ltd
This edition published 2017
1 3 5 7 9 10 8 6 4 2

Centum Books Ltd, 20 Devon Square,
Newton Abbot, Devon, TQ12 2HR, UK

books@centumbooksltd.co.uk

CENTUM BOOKS Limited Reg. No. 07641486

A CIP catalogue record for this book is
available from the British Library

Printed in Italy

centum

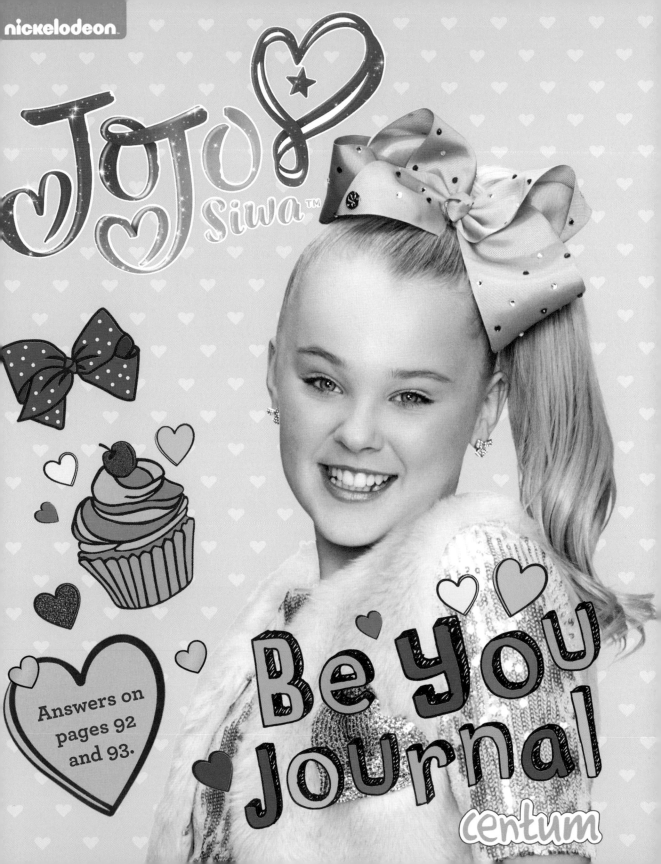

nickelodeon

JoJo Siwa™

Answers on pages 92 and 93.

Be You Journal

centum

Contents

There's so much fun inside, including:

BE You

Super Cute

DREAM
Crazy
BIG

All about me

Fill these pages with all the cute, cool and crazy things about you and your life.

name: ....

nickname: ....

birthday: ....

age: ....

year born: ....

star sign: ....

home town/city: ....

BFF: ....

pets: ....

SWEET

Most embarrassing moment EVER:

....

....

....

Biggest achievement:

....

....

Proudest moment:

....

....

....

Best thing about me:

....

....

....

....

....

Be you

Only my (mum/dad/best friend/ sister/brother) knows that I:

....

....

....

Fave things

Fill this page with all your fave things.

friend:..

family member:..

movie:..

TV show:...

vlogger:..

choccy bar:...

song: ....

shop:..

animal: ....

sport: ....

food:...

drink: ....

time of year:..

day of the week:...

The thing I love doing most in the world is:

....

....

....

DID YOU KNOW JOJO'S FAVOURITE DESSERT IS SHAVED ICE?

The first thing I do after I get up is:

....

....

....

....

The best part of the day is when I:

....

....

BowBow

The last thing I do before I go to sleep is:

....

....

My life

Use this page to write about what you do on a typical day each week.

★★★★	morning	afternoon	evening
Monday			
Tuesday			
Wednesday			
Thursday			
Friday			
Saturday			
Sunday			

Wake up at:

School starts at:

Eat lunch at:

Finish school:

Eat dinner at:

Go to sleep at:

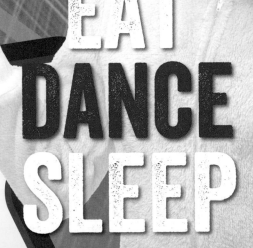

DID YOU KNOW JOJO'S FAVOURITE SUBJECT IS MATHS?!

EAT
DANCE
SLEEP

Family tree

Fill in your family tree with names, pics or doodles to show who's who in your family.

Who is the cuddliest:

....

Who is the loudest:

....

Who is the happiest:

....

Who is the messiest:

....

Who is the funniest:

....

Who is the chattiest:

....

Who is the cutest:

....

SWEET

Who is the smartest:

....

15

BFFs

Which of your pals is your best mate:

....

kindest pal:

....

funniest friend:

....

oldest friend:

....

Which of your friends is the
best dancer:

....

most organised:

....

best shopper:

....

most scatterbrained:

....

WHO IS MOST LIKE
JOJO IN YOUR
FRIENDSHIP GROUP?

BFF gallery

Fill these pages with pics of you and your BFFs, or doodle pics!

SWEET

JOJO LOVES HER PET DOG BOWBOW. CAN DOGS BE BFFS? DEFINITELY!

19

Friendship *quiz*

Take this quick quiz to find out if you and your friend will be BFFs.

1. How long have you and your mate been friends for?

- A   seems like forever ♡
- B   a couple of years ♡
- C   a few months ♡

2. How often do you see your friend?

- A   every day ♡
- B   a few times a month ♡
- C   hardly ever ♡

3. Do you and your friend ever fall out?

- A   hardly and just over silly things ♡
- B   quite often ♡
- C   we argue most days ♡

4. If your friend had a bad hair day, what would you do?

- A   help her restyle it ♡
- B   lend her a hat to cover it up ♡
- C   refuse to be seen with her ♡

5. Have you ever forgotten your friend's birthday?

    A   never, it's written in my diary ♡

    B   sometimes, but I always
       make it up to them ♡

    C   I forget every year! ♡

6. Do you keep your friend's secrets?

    A   always ♡

    B   usually, unless I forget and tell
       someone by mistake ♡

    C   sometimes, but I often end up
       telling other friends too ♡

7. If your friend copies you, what do you do?

    A   laugh but like it that we're
       the same ♡

    B   feel embarrassed but try to
       ignore it ♡

    C   get really mad and tell her to stop ♡

DISCOVER YOUR
RATING ON THE
NEXT PAGE!

Friendship *quiz*

How did you do?

Mostly As
You and your friend are two of a kind and will be best friends for life!

Mostly Bs
You're great pals but you like to hang out with other friends too.

Mostly Cs
Hmmm, sounds like you're good friends but not best friends.

JOJO LOVES HAVING HER FRIENDS JOIN HER ON HER YOUTUBE CHANNEL

Odd cupcake out

Which one of these cupcakes
isn't like the rest?
Can you spot the odd one out?

Answer on p92.

Word power

Which of these JoJo-inspired words describe you?
Tick as many as you want!

Sweet

Confident

Positive

Awesome

Crazy

Happy

Dreamer

Sassy

Cute

Super

Hopeful

Chilled

Energetic

Achiever

DREAM CRAZY BIG

Bow crazy

Count all the bows on these pages.
How many can you count of each design?

WHICH BOW IS YOUR FAVOURITE?

Answer on p92.

Seek and find

Can you spot all the cute words below in the grid opposite?

SWEET

PUFF

GIGGLE

TWINKLE

WARM

CUDDLE

SPARKLE

CUTE

FLUFFY

BOWBOW

28

W	B	C	U	D	D	L	E	K	M	P	V
X	B	R	H	G	L	A	Y	R	Q	O	F
T	A	O	F	M	U	N	A	X	W	D	B
W	Z	E	W	I	T	W	D	L	S	K	S
I	F	K	C	B	M	E	Z	R	C	U	P
N	L	D	W	Q	O	T	D	B	U	S	A
K	P	X	N	U	S	W	E	E	T	G	R
L	W	T	R	Y	I	A	X	J	E	M	K
E	N	G	J	P	O	C	T	Y	L	E	L
J	T	W	A	U	E	G	I	G	G	L	E
F	L	U	F	F	Y	I	P	Z	H	J	P
D	F	I	S	F	Z	G	J	E	P	W	I

SUPER CUTE

Answer on p92.

29

Animal cuties

JoJo loves her cute dog BowBow! Number the animals on these pages from 1 to 20, with 1 for the most cute and 20 for the least.

Panda

Elephant

Piglet

Duckling

Kitten

Puppy

Mouse

Owl

Squirrel

Chick

Whale

Shark

Ladybird

Bumblebee

Monkey

Worm

Seal

Hedgehog

Goldfish

Parrot

31

JoJo spotting

These small pictures of me opposite may all look the same as the big picture, but something is different in each one. Can you spot what?

a.

b.

c.

d.

Answer on p92.

Cutie cut-outs

Cut out all the cute pics on the following pages and use them to decorate your notebook, diary, bedroom or school locker.

BOWS
MAKE
EVERYTHING
BETTER

34

DREAM **Crazy** **BIG**

DREAM **Crazy** **BIG**

DREAM **Crazy** **BIG**

CUTE & CONFIDENT

CUTE & CONFIDENT

CUTE & CONFIDENT

Super Cute

Super Cute

Super Cute

This book belongs to:

This book belongs to:

This book belongs to:

This book belongs to:

This book belongs to:

This book belongs to:

TOP SECRET!

TOP SECRET!

TOP SECRET!

I ♥ my BFF

I ♥ my BFF

I ♥ my BFF

DO NOT DISTURB

DO NOT DISTURB

DO NOT DISTURB

Chill Out!

Chill Out!

Chill Out!

BE You

BE You

BE You

Sweet tweets!

Check out these JoJo-inspired hashtags, then write your own below.

#BestiesNotBullies
#PeaceOutHaterz
#BeYourSelfie
#ICanMakeYouDance
#JoJosJuice

#..

#..

#..

#..

#..

#..

#..

#..

#..

#..

Vlog it?

If you could have your own YouTube channel, just like JoJo, what would you vlog about? Come up with some super-awesome ideas that are important to you.

1.

Vlog idea:..

Main points to talk about:.................................

....

Props needed:..

2.

Vlog idea:..

Main points to talk about:.................................

....

Props needed:..

3.

Vlog idea:..

Main points to talk about:.................................

....

Props needed:..

4. Vlog idea:...

Main points to talk about:.......................................

....

Props needed:...

5. Vlog idea:...

Main points to talk about:.......................................

....

Props needed:...

DID YOU KNOW
THAT JOJO ENDS EVERY
VLOG BY THROWING
JUICE OVER HER HEAD?
THAT'S WHY HER CHANNEL
IS CALLED JOJO'S JUICE.

JOJO'S JUICE

House tour!

JoJo loves telling her fans all about her life – some of her favourite vlogs are house tours!

Draw your house in this frame and label your favourite parts.

Write down five awesome facts about your home:

1. ....

2. ....

3. ....

4. ....

5. ....

Closet cool

What does your dream closet look like? Draw it below and organise your clothes and accessories!

DID YOU SEE JOJO'S CLOSET TOUR VLOG? #GOALS

Will you organise by colour or type?

45

Recipe time!

Follow the simple steps here to create some yummy, scrummy cookies. These cookies are perfect for a sleepover with your BFFs.

RECIPES SHOULD BE DONE WITH AN ADULT'S PERMISSION AND SUPERVISION.

YOU WILL NEED:

★ 100g butter (softened)
★ 125g caster sugar
★ 1 large free-range egg
★ 1 teaspoon vanilla extract
★ 200g self-raising flour
★ 100g chocolate chips or chocolate (broken up)

1. Preheat the oven to 170°C/325°F/gas mark 3 and line two baking sheets with greaseproof paper.

2. Beat the butter and sugar together in a bowl.

3. Crack in the egg, add the vanilla and mix.

4. Sift in the flour and stir in the chocolate chips.

5. Roll a tablespoon's worth of the dough into small balls and pop on to the lined trays.

6. Chill in the fridge for 20 minutes, then push the balls flat with your fingers and place in the oven for 10 to 12 minutes.

7. Take out and leave to cool for a few minutes, then tuck in.

EAT DANCE SLEEP

Fave foods!

List all your favourite foods on this page! Who would you invite to your dream dinner party? (JoJo, of course!)

Favourite fruits: ....

....

Favourite vegetables: ....

....

Lunchbox essentials: ....

....

Favourite snacks: ....

....

Favourite international foods:..

....

Foods I want to try:..

Favourite foods to share:..

DID YOU KNOW JOJO LOVES CHICKEN WINGS?
SHE HATES HAMBURGERS AND HOT DOGS.

DREAM Crazy BIG

JoJo has always tried to follow her dreams and achieve her goals! She tells everyone to dream, crazy, big! In this section write down your hopes and dreams for the future.

WHY NOT TAPE THIS SECTION TOGETHER, THEN OPEN IT UP AGAIN IN THE FUTURE AND DISCOVER IF YOUR DREAMS CAME TRUE?

Daydreamer

What do you daydream about most?

school

clothes

friends

holidays

celebs

food

ghosts

TV shows

movies

dancing

family

pets

Dream home

My dream home would be a:

mansion ♡
castle ♡
city flat ♡
ranch ♡
farm ♡
yacht ♡
caravan ♡
beach house ♡

My dream home would be:

next door to my BFF ♡
around the corner from where I live now ♡
up a mountain ♡
on a beach ♡
on a lake ♡
next to a river ♡
in a forest ♡
in the countryside ♡

Doodle your fave daydream in this bubble.

My dream home would be in:

UK ♡
Europe ♡
Asia ♡
Australia ♡
North America ♡
South America ♡
Africa ♡
Antarctica ♡
Arctic ♡

51

Dream holiday

What would your dream holiday be like?

My dream holiday would be in:

UK ♡
Europe ♡
Asia ♡
Australia ♡
North America ♡
South America ♡
Africa ♡
Antarctica ♡
Arctic ♡

I would travel by:

bike ♡
boat ♡
plane ♡
helicopter ♡
car ♡
submarine ♡

I would stay in a:

hotel ♡
caravan ♡
apartment ♡
castle ♡

I would eat:

fruit ♡
pizza ♡
ice cream ♡
sweets ♡

Dream job

What would your dream job be?

I would love to work with:

animals ♡

children ♡

only my friends ♡

on my own ♡

I would love to work:

in an office ♡

in a dance studio ♡

on the beach ♡

in a garden ♡

in a shop ♡

in a vehicle ♡

in a foreign country ♡

in space ♡

in the jungle ♡

Number these jobs from 1 to 12, with 1 being the one you'd most like to do and 12 the least.

vet

astronaut

teacher

TV presenter

doctor

vlogger

dancer

actor

engineer

marine biologist

firefighter

pilot

Decode your dreams!

Ever wondered what your dreams mean? Write about the last dream you remember below. Was it weird, crazy, scary, exciting or fun?

If you dream you are FALLING from the sky, down a hole or off a cliff, it can mean you feel out of control. Try to work out what area of your life you need to take control of, and what you can do about it.

If you dream you are FLYING, it means you feel confident and secure about your life and in control. If you dream you are flying too high, it can mean you are concerned how your success might change your life.

If you dream you are BEING CHASED, it means you have a problem in your life that you need to face up to and deal with.

WHATEVER YOUR DREAMS MIGHT MEAN, JUST REMEMBER TO DREAM BIG, JUST LIKE JOJO!

Your dream year

January

....
....
....

February

....
....
....

March

....
....
....

April

....
....
....

May

....
....
....

June

....
....
....

July

....
....
....

August

....
....
....

September

....
....
....

October

....
....

November

....
....

December

....
....

My future

In 1 year I hope:...
....
....
....
....
....

In 3 years I hope:...
....
....
....
....

58

In 5 years I hope:..
....
....
....
....
....

In 10 years I hope:..
....
....
....
....
....

NOW SEAL THIS SECTION WITH TAPE AND

OPEN IT AGAIN IN THE FUTURE!

Copy draw

Copy and draw the cute pics on to the grids on these pages.

DID YOU KNOW THAT JOJO LOVES TO PAINT AND DRAW? ART RULEZ!

61

Rule the school!

Fill this page with all your fave things about your school!

name of your school:

....

fave subject:..

fave teacher: ....

most amazing thing you've

learned this year: ....

....

....

....

Number these subjects from 1 to 9, with 1 your most fave subject and 9 your least.

English

Science

Drama

Maths

Geography

PE

History

Music

Art

Technology

Use the space above to design a super-cute school uniform.

DON'T FORGET YOUR SCHOOL BAG!

Muddled lines

Hurry, JoJo needs juice for her latest vlog! Which line leads her to the juice?

a.

b.

c.

SWEET

JoJo's Juice

JoJo's Juice

Happy holidays

Tick which type of holiday you've been on and circle the ones you'd love to try!

camping

beach

sightseeing

safari

activity

diving

skiing

cooking

horse riding

Other:

....

....

cruise

....

....

cycling

....

Best holiday memory ever:

....

....

If I could go on holiday with anyone, I would go with:

....

....

Worst holiday memory ever:

....

....

Name three places you have been to on holiday:

....

....

....

Name three places you would love to go on holiday:

....

....

....

Get ready for your next holiday with your top 5 items to pack:

....

....

....

....

....

Design your own cute suitcase to take on your next holiday.

67

Create your own blog

Use the spaces on these pages to plan your own blog or website, just like JoJo's.

Step 1 Think of a name or handle for your site:

www. ....

@ ....

Step 2 Design a logo and your masthead (the picture at the top of your site):

68

Step 3 — What kind of things would you blog about?

- fashion
- friends
- music
- books
- movies
- TV shows
- politics
- animals
- travel
- art
- news
- other: ....

Step 4

Decide how often will you post?

- every day ♡
- once a week ♡
- once a month ♡

DON'T FORGET TO ALWAYS ASK A GROWN-UP BEFORE YOU GO ONLINE!

Step 5

Make sure you include popular hashtags to help share your content:

....

....

....

Step 6

Decide who you will share your blog with and ask them to give you a mark out of 10.

- family ♡
- friends ♡
- teachers ♡

Fashion haul

Which of the items below do want to add to your wardrobe?

If you did a JoJo-inspired fashion haul, which clothes would be on your fashion hit list? Create your dream haul on these pages.

jeans

shorts

culottes

dress

jumper

mini skirt

maxi skirt

jacket

dungarees

skirt

leggings

trousers

waistcoat

T-shirt

hat

Tick all the colours you love to wear:

Where do you like to shop for...?

something fancy:

....

chill-out clothes:

....

sportswear:

....

accessories:

....

something different:

....

DID YOU KNOW JOJO'S FAVOURITE COLOUR IS GLITTER!

Design your dream outfit in this box:

JOJO HAS HER OWN UNIQUE SENSE OF STYLE! HOW WOULD YOU DESCRIBE YOURS?

My routine

Fill out the chart to discover more about your routine. How often do you do the following?

	every day	twice a day	once a week	twice a week	once a month	never
wash your hair						
brush your hair						
brush your teeth						
get a haircut						
paint your nails						
take a selfie						
hang with your BFF						
watch TV						
play a video game						
go for a walk						
do exercise						
learn a new fact						
dream about the future						

What are your good habits?

....

....

....

....

....

JOJO PRACTISES DANCE ROUTINES MOST DAYS A WEEK!

EAT DANCE SLEEP

Do you have any bad habits?

....

....

....

....

....

Perfect pairs

Can you draw lines between all the pairs that match?

Answer on p93.

Happy birthday!

Never forget a BFF's birthday again. Write down the birthdays of your loved ones on these pages.

name:...

birthday:..

age:..

star sign:..

perfect present:
....
....

perfect present:
....
....

name:...

birthday:..

age:..

star sign:..

name:...

birthday:..

age:..

star sign:..

perfect present:
....
....

perfect present:
....
....

name: ....
birthday: ....
age: ....
star sign: ....

name: ....
birthday: ....
age: ....
star sign: ....

perfect present:
....
....

perfect present:
....
....

name: ....
birthday: ....
age: ....
star sign: ....

name: ....
birthday: ....
age: ....
star sign: ....

perfect present:
....
....

perfect present:
....
....

name: ....
birthday: ....
age: ....
star sign: ....

name: ....
birthday: ....
age: ....
star sign: ....

perfect present:
....
....

perfect present:
....
....

name: ....
birthday: ....
age: ....
star sign: ....

name: ....
birthday: ....
age: ....
star sign: ....

perfect present:
....
....

perfect present:

....

....

name: ....

birthday: ....

age: ....

star sign: ....

name: ....

birthday: ....

age: ....

star sign: ....

perfect present:

....

....

perfect present:

....

....

name: ....

birthday: ....

age: ....

star sign: ....

DON'T FORGET JOJO'S BIRTHDAY!

name: JoJo Siwa

birthday: 19th May 2003

age: 14

star sign: TAURUS

perfect present: BOWS, NATURALLY!

79

Colouring competition

Colour all the cute stuff on these pages. Ask each of your friends to colour in something, then pick your favourite!

From My Heart To Yours

Party fun

JOJO LOVES PARTIES – ESPECIALLY IF THERE'S DANCING INVOLVED AND LOTS AND LOTS OF GLITTER!

Birthdays are the best, right?! Even if your next one isn't till next year, it's never too early to start planning a party!

Step 1

Make a party invite list:

....
....
....
....
....
....
....
....
....

Step 2

Create a present wish list:

....
....
....

Step 3

Decide on a party theme:

pizza	♡	sleepover	♡
bowling	♡	swimming	♡
dance	♡	baking	♡
karaoke	♡	cinema	♡
beauty	♡		

CHECK OUT THESE COOL INVITES!

 82

Continued on page 87.

....

IS HAVING A PARTY AND
WOULD LOVE YOU TO COME!

WHEN: ....
WHERE: ....

....
TIME: ....
RSVP: ....

....

IS HAVING A PARTY AND
WOULD LOVE YOU TO COME!

WHEN: ....
WHERE: ....

....
TIME: ....
RSVP: ....

....

IS HAVING A PARTY AND
WOULD LOVE YOU TO COME!

WHEN: ....
WHERE: ....

....
TIME: ....
RSVP: ....

....

IS HAVING A PARTY AND
WOULD LOVE YOU TO COME!

WHEN: ....
WHERE: ....

....
TIME: ....
RSVP: ....

Invite

To:

JoJo Siwa™

© Viacom

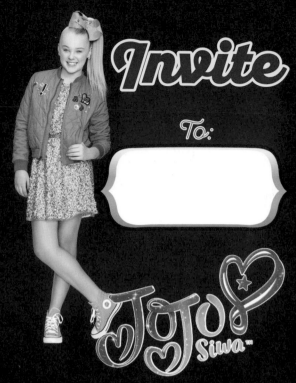

Invite

To:

JoJo Siwa™

© Viacom

Invite

To:

JoJo Siwa™

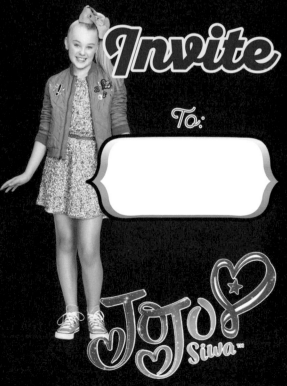

Invite

To:

JoJo Siwa™

© Viacom

IS HAVING A PARTY AND
WOULD LOVE YOU TO COME!

WHEN: ....
WHERE: ....

....
TIME: ....
RSVP: ....

IS HAVING A PARTY AND
WOULD LOVE YOU TO COME!

WHEN: ....
WHERE: ....

....
TIME: ....
RSVP: ....

IS HAVING A PARTY AND
WOULD LOVE YOU TO COME!

WHEN: ....
WHERE: ....

....
TIME: ....
RSVP: ....

IS HAVING A PARTY AND
WOULD LOVE YOU TO COME!

WHEN: ....
WHERE: ....

....
TIME: ....
RSVP: ....

Invite

To:

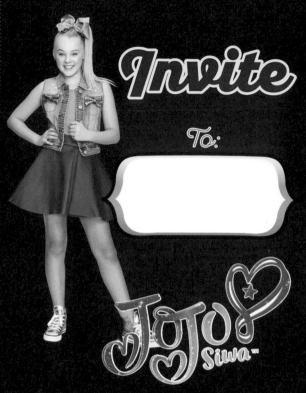

Invite

To:

© Viacom

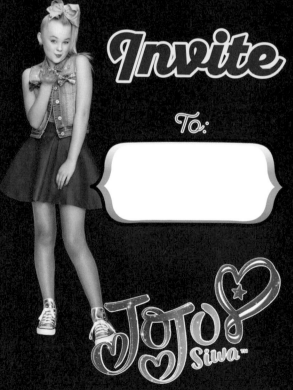

Invite

To:

Invite

To:

© Viacom

© Viacom

Continued from page 82.

Step 4

What time will the party start and end?

Start:

Finish:

Step 5

Design the perfect party outfit below.

87

Bow designer

JoJo has so many bows because

BOWS ARE EVERYTHING!

Design JoJo a new bow on the template below, then design one for yourself on the page opposite.

BOWS ARE MY SUPER POWER

DID YOU KNOW JOJO HAS NEARLY 1,000 BOWS?! WHOA!

Fan mail

JoJo loves getting fan mail! Write a letter to her on this page.

From My Heart To Yours

Dear JoJo,

Siwanator Pledge

Are you a Siwanator? If you're a fan of JoJo, then that's what you call yourself! Read the Siwanator pledge below and channel your inner JoJo.

Siwanatorz everywhere pledge to:

Be confident and strong.

Walk away from the haters and bullies.

Look out for fellow Siwanators.

Be kind to everyone, even the haters.

Never give up. Girls never quit.

Always be your selfie!

And, most importantly,

respect the bow!

JOJO Siwa

Answers

Page 23

 a.

 b.

 c.

 d.

 e.

 f.

Pages 26–27

 2

 4

 3

 6

 3

 5

Pages 28–29

W	B	C	U	D	D	L	E	K	M	P	V
X	B	R	H	G	L	A	Y	R	Q	O	F
T	A	O	F	M	U	N	A	X	W	D	B
W	Z	E	W	I	T	W	D	L	S	K	S
I	F	K	C	B	M	E	Z	R	C	U	P
N	L	D	W	Q	O	T	D	B	U	S	A
K	P	X	N	U	S	W	E	E	T	G	R
L	W	T	R	Y	I	A	X	J	E	M	K
E	N	G	J	P	O	C	T	Y	L	E	L
J	T	W	A	U	E	G	I	G	G	L	E
F	L	U	F	F	Y	I	P	Z	H	J	P
D	F	I	S	F	Z	G	J	E	P	W	I

Pages 32–33

 a.

 b.

 c.

 d.

Pages 64–65

a.
b.
c.

Pages 74–75